HENRY PURCELL

CHACONY
CHACONNE

for Strings
für Streicher
Edited by/Herausgegeben von
Walter Bergmann

Ernst Eulenburg Ltd
London · Mainz · New York · Paris · Tokyo · Zürich

HENRY PURCELL
Chacony

The only source of the Chacony is Purcell's autograph score book in the British Library (Add. MS 30930)[1]. From the position in this book and from stylistic evidence the Chacony seems to have been composed between 1680, the date of his fifteen Fantazias (in the traditional English style), and 1683, the year when his twelve Trio-'Sonnata's of III parts in imitation of the . . . Italian masters' were published.

We do not know why Purcell named the work Chacony. The assumption that this was the old English term for chaconne[2] has not been proved. I have come across only one other Chacony: in the libretto to Purcell's *Dido and Aeneas* 'A Dance Gittars Chacony' is mentioned. This, however, is not extant, if it ever was written[3]. Purcell's own spelling of chaconne was 'chacone'. Was Chacony the mispronounciation of this misspelling? Or did Purcell intend to distinguish between this composition and a danceable chaconne? We know that he loathed 'the levity and balladry'[4] of the French music. Also, this Chacony was never intended to be danced to. Though it starts with a regular eight-bar ground, the periods are broken up at bar 54 when the seventh repeat of the ground is overlapped by the eighth, reducing the seventh to five bars, and also at bars 109-113 and 122 when six bars unrelated to the ground are interspersed. One could not dance to such irregularities. The lively rhythmic independence of the middle parts also argues strongly against the conception of the Chacony as a dance and for it as a purely instrumental piece.

We do not know for whom and for what instruments the Chacony was composed, except that it cannot have been intended for instruments other than strings. The clefs in which it is written fit both viols and the violin family. The mezzo-soprano clef on the third line does not preclude the use of a viola, rather the contrary. It served for the violinists (who were familiar only with the treble clef) as a kind of tabulature for playing on the viola; they just had to imagine that they had a violin in their hands and that they read the music in the treble clef:

Thus the Chacony could serve as music for a string quartet or for a string orchestra (e.g. the Royal 24 Violinists) or for a consort of viols, or even a broken consort of violins and viols. In modern times the Chacony has been played by string quartets as well as by string orchestras.

---

[1] Add. MS 33236 fol. 65 contains a late 17th-century copy of just the title (*Chacony*) and the first fourteen bars of the two upper parts.

[2] Groves, *Dictionary of Music*, 5th edition, London 1954.

[3] Franklin Zimmerman, *Henry Purcell, Analytical catalogue*, London 1963, p. 298.

[4] Preface to the *Sonnata's of Three parts*, Eulenburg Ed. No. 1353.

IV

The interpretation of the music raises many questions, among which are the tempo, the so-called double-dotting, the use of a keyboard continuo instrument, and the slurs. The much-quoted Quantz[5] suggests crotchet $= 160$ as the tempo of a chaconne and he also says that in the chaconne the quaver after a dot should not be played according to its metrical value but very short and sharp. Neither statement applies to Purcell's Chacony, firstly because of the time lag of seventy years between its composition and Quantz's book, and secondly because Quantz was directing his remarks explicitly at the French dance music[6]. As explained above, the Chacony is neither dance music nor composed in the French style. As far as the tempo is concerned it is quite obvious that crotchet $= 160$ is far too short for the Chacony; on the other hand too slow a tempo will deprive passages like ♩ ♫ ♫ ♩ and ♫♫♫ of the Purcellian vigour and brilliance. A tempo of crotchet$=c.$ 100 seems the most suitable speed to bring out both the spirit and the delicacies of the score.

The term 'double-dotting' (a rather unsatisfactory term) refers to the fact that until the middle of the eighteenth century the notation of a double dot after a note was unknown and that therefore a single dot ♩. ♪ could mean either what it said or a ♩.. ♪ rhythm. The discovery of this fact in the first half of the twentieth century was followed by an excess of double dotting. The print of the Chacony in the Purcell Society Edition[7] suggests no less than 302 rhythmic alterations of Purcell's autograph within its 154 bars. A performance in that manner would lead to musically unacceptable results as a simple attempt, extended over the whole work, will show. Disciples of the excessive double-dotting method are reminded of the fact that Purcell could write an equivalent of a double dot; indeed he has done so repeatedly, for instance in bars 120 and 121 of the Chacony, several times in the Symphony at the beginning of the *Ode for St. Cecilia's Day, 1683 'Welcome to all the Pleasures'*[8] (where ♩ ♫ and ♩. ♪ appear with different rhythmic significance even in the same bar), and in *A Serenading Song*[9] etc. Apart from these examples there is ample proof that Purcell used rhythms like ♫♫♫ in one part concurrently with ♫♫ in another with brilliant results. The rhythmic unification as aimed at in the print of the Chacony in the Purcell Society Edition makes no allowance to such Purcellian subtleties.

The question to dot or double dot cannot be answered generally; it has to be decided individually from bar to bar and can be decided variously by different performers. In the opinion of the editor the quaver is supreme in the Chacony and should only very occasionally be adjusted to the semiquavers appearing in other parts. The semiquavers themselves, being the shortest notes in the Chacony, should not be played in their metrical value after a dot but very short; they will contrast well with the quavers in passages like bar 62ff. and others. However, such matters are best left to the taste and instinct of the

---

[5] J. J. Quantz, *Versuch einer Anweisung die Flöte traversiere zu spielen*, 1752, XVII section 7 para. 58.

[6] op. cit. para. 56.

[7] Vol. XXXI 1959, p. 61ff.

[8] Eulenburg Edition No. 1062.

[9] *Orpheus Britannicus*, 1698 p. 14.

performer, and therefore Purcell's text has here been printed without alteration.

The question whether the fourth stave of the score should be read as a basso continuo line (unfigured), and whether the performance of the Chacony should therefore include the use of a keyboard instrument as suggested by the editor of the Purcell Society Edition, must be answered in the negative. Historical considerations apart, this would not only be unnecessary, for the Chacony as it stands is complete, but may also dangerously interfere with Purcell's lively independent middle parts.

In the text the ties are quite clear, but regarding the slurs it is sometimes doubtful whether they cover two or three notes. However, either decision will not be of any great consequence.

Editorial Notes

The present edition gives Purcell's autograph text with the following exceptions:

Accidentals modernised and valid for a bar. Editorial accidentals in square brackets.

Dots after barlines replaced by tied quavers.

Purcell's sign for a trill is 𝆓 𝆒. It has been supplemented by [tr].

b69 Vla crotchet rest replaces dot after minim

bb4 & 32 Vl I slurs unclear in AUT

bb141 & 149 Vl II slurs unclear in AUT

Walter Bergmann

HENRY PURCELL

Chacony

Die einzige Quelle für Purcells Chacony ist die Autographpartitur im Sammelband Add. MS 30930 der British Library in London[1]. Aus äusseren und stilistischen Gründen ist anzunehmen, dass die Chacony zwischen 1680 – dem Jahr der Purcellschen Fantasien – und 1683 – dem Publikationsjahr der 12 Triosonaten nach italienischem Muster – entstanden ist.

Warum Purcell das Werk 'Chacony' nannte, ist unbekannt. Dass dies ein altenglischer Name für Chaconne sei, wie Grove[2] annahm, entbehrt jeden Beweises. Im Libretto zu Purcells *Dido and Aeneas* ist zwar eine 'Dance Gittars Chacony' erwähnt, aber mehr wissen wir nicht darüber[3]. Purcell selbst schrieb Chaconne nur mit einem N. Sprach er 'chacone' vielleicht als Chacony aus? Oder wollte er damit einen Unterschied zwischen seiner und der französischen Chaconne machen? Wir wissen, dass er die 'Frivolität und Balladerei'[4] der französischen Musik nicht leiden konnte. Auch war, im Gegensatz zur Chaconne, die Chacony nicht tanzbar. Sie fängt zwar auf einem regelmässigen, acht-taktigen Ostinato an, aber bei Takt 54 überschneiden sich die siebente und achte Wiederholung und bei den Takten 109-113 und 122 werden sechs freie Takte eingeschoben. Zu solchen Unregelmässigkeiten konnte man nicht tanzen. Der ganze Aufbau der Chacony und insbesondere die rhythmische Freiheit der Mittelstimmen sprechen dafür, dass die Chacony als reine Instrumentalmusik geplant war.

Wir wissen nicht, für wen die Chacony komponiert war, nicht einmal für welche Instrumente, nur dass offenbar keine anderen Instrumente als Streichinstrumente in Frage kommen. Die Schlüssel passen sowohl auf die Gamben- wie auf die Geigenfamilie. Dass die dritte Stimme im Mezzosopranschlüssel steht, spricht nicht gegen letztere, im Gegenteil. Der Mezzosopranschlüssel konnte einem Geiger als eine Art Tabulatur dienen, mit deren Hilfe er ohne Kenntnis des Altschlüssels auf der (damals noch seltenen) Bratsche zu spielen: er brauchte sich nur vorzustellen, dass er keine Bratsche sondern eine Violine in der Hand hätte, und Konnte dann die Stimme im Violinschlüssel lesen:

So konnte die Chacony für Streichquartet, Streichorchester (z.B. des Königs 24 Violinisten), für ein Gambenensemble oder ein aus Geigen und Gamben gemischtes Ensemble dienen. Heutzutage wird die Chacony hauptsächlich von Streichquartetten und Streichorchestern gespielt.

[1] British Library Add. MS 33236 fol. 65 enthält eine Kopie des Titels (*Chacony*) und der ersten 14 Takte der beiden Oberstimmen.

[2] Grove's *Dictionary of Music and Musicians*, 5. Auflage, London, 1954.

[3] Franklin Zimmerman, *Henry Purcell, Analytical Catalogue*, London 1963, S.298.

[4] Vorwort zu den *Sonnata's of Three parts*. Eulenburg Edition. Nr. 1353.

Die musikalische Interpretation der Chacony bietet einige Probleme, unter
denen das Tempo, die Doppelpunktierung, der Gebrauch eines continuo
Instruments und die Bindebögen hervorragen. Als Tempo für eine Chaconne
gibt der viel zitierte Quantz[5] ♩ = 160 an; er verlangt weiterhin, dass in einer
Chaconne die Achtel nach punktierten Viertelnoten 'nicht nach ihrer eigent-
lichen Geltung, sondern sehr kurz und scharf gespielet werden'. Beide
Vorschriften treffen jedoch auf die Chacony nicht zu, einmal wegen des
Zeitablaufes von 70 Jahren zwischen der Komposition der Chacony und
Quantzs Buch, und zweitens weil Quantz ausdrücklich nur von der franzö-
sischen Tanzmusik geschrieben hat[6]. Wie oben erwähnt, ist die Chacony weder
Tanzmusik noch französisch. Was das Zeitmass betrifft, ist ♩ = 160 offen-
sichtlich viel zu schnell für die Chacony. Andererseits nimmt ein zu langsames
Tempo Passagen wie ♩. ♫ ♫. ♩ und ♫♫♫ ihre so typisch Purcellsche
Kraft und Brilluanz. Ein Zeitmass von ungefähr ♩ = 100 scheint am besten
geeignet, die Stärke und die Feinheiten der Partitur aufzuzeigen.

Der Ausdruck 'Doppelpunktierung' bezieht sich darauf, dass der Doppelpunkt
nach einer Note zu Purcells Zeiten noch unbekannt war. Ein Punkt hinter
einer Note konnte daher bedeuten was er besagt, ♩. ♪ oder aber auch einen
Rhythmus wie ♩.. ♪ Diese Entdeckung, die in der ersten Hälfte des 20ten
Jahrhunderts populär wurde, führte zu einem Exzess im Doppelpunktieren,
dem auch die Chacony in der Ausgabe der Purcell Society[7] zum Opfer fiel. In
den 154 Takten der Chacony sind dort nicht weniger als 302 rhythmische
Änderungen des Purcellschen Textes vorgeschlagen. Eine Aufführung dieser
Art würde zu musikalisch unhaltbaren Folgerungen führen, wie jeder Versuch
zeigen wird. Dabei haben die Anhänger des exzessuven Gebrauchs des Doppelpunktes übersehen, dass Purcell ein Äquivalent des Doppelpunktes schreiben
konnte und geschrieben hat. Vgl. z. B. Takt 120, 121 der Chacony oder den lang-
samen Einleitungssatz zur *Ode for St. Cecilia's Day, 1683*[8], wo ♩ ♩. ♩ und ♩. ♪
gleichzeitig aber gegensätzlich in ein und demselben Takt gebraucht werden,
oder ähnliche Stellen im *A Serenading Song*[9]. Wir haben hinreichende
Beweis dafür, dass Purcell Rhythmen wie ♫♫ in einer Stimme gleichzeitig
mit ♫♫ in einer anderen gebrauchte. Die Gleichsetzung solcher Rhythmen,
wie in der Purcell Society Ausgabe propagiert, wird den Feinheiten Purcell-
scher Polyrhythmic nicht gerecht. Auf die Frage, wann ein Komponist eine
einfache und wann er eine Doppelpunktierung beabsichtigte, gibt es keine
generelle Antwort; die Frage muss von Fall zu Fall entschieden werden und
kann von verschiedenen Ausführenden verschieden beantwortet werden. In
der Chacony dominiert in der Ansicht des Herausgebers die Achtelnote, die
nur sehr gelegentlich den Sechzehnteln in andern Stimmen angeglichen werden sollte. Die Sechzehntel selbst, als die kürzesten Noten der Chacony,
müssen nach einem Punkt nicht nach ihrem metrischen Wert sondern sehr
kurz gespielt werden, wodurch die in Passagen wie 62ff. und anderswo brilliant

[5] J. J. Quantz, *Versuch einer Anweisung die Flöte traversiere zu spielen*, 1752, XVII. Hauptstück,
7. Abschnitt, Paragraph 58.

[6] wie Nr. 5, Paragraph 56.

[7] Band XXXI (1959) S.61 fol.

[8] Eulenburg Edition Nr. 1062

[9] *Orpheus Britannicus*, 1698, S.14

mit den Achtelnoten kontrastieren. Da die Lösung solcher Probleme sehr vom Geschmack, Instinkt und der Kenntnis der Spieler (und Herausgeber) abhängt, bringt die vorliegende Ausgabe die Chacony ohne Änderung in der Purcellschen Notierung.

Der Ansicht des Herausgebers der Purcell Society Ausgabe, dass die Bassstimme der Chacony als basso continuo-Stimme zu behandeln sei und deshalb ein Tasteninstrument gebraucht werden müsse, kann nicht zugestimmt werden. Ganz abgesehen von historischen Erwägungen ist eine Vermehrung der Stimmen nicht nur unnötig, da die Chacony vollkommen in sich selbst ist, sondern würde auch störend auf die selbständigen Mittelstimmen einwirken.

Im Gegensatz zu den Haltebögen ist es bei den Legatobögen gelegentlich zweifelhaft, ob sie zwei oder drei Noten umfassen. In beiden Fällen ist die Entscheidung hierüber nicht von wesentlicher Bedeutung.

Walter Bergmann

CHACONY

Henry Purcell
1659-1695

Ernst Eulenburg Ltd

2

4

5

6